The GIANT PANDA

The GIANT PANDA

Philip Steele
Illustrated by John Butler

Kingfisher

About this book

The **Giant Panda** is almost like two books in one – a storybook to read and an information book to explore. Large, colourful illustrations and a simple narrative tell the story of the panda's life in the wild, while the text under the folds provides a mine of fascinating information.

If you are reading with a child, the underfold facts will give you the perfect opportunity to pause, answer questions and discuss what is happening in the story.

Children reading alone, will enjoy discovering the extra details under the folds, especially as the information they find there will enhance their understanding of the story.

After reading **The Giant Panda**, you may like to find out more about protecting pandas in the wild. If so, why not contact the local branch of an organization, such as the World Wide Fund for Nature, for more information.

It is dawn in the misty mountains of southwest China and a giant panda has just woken up from a deep restful sleep. She stretches and yawns, baring her pointed yellow teeth. Then she grabs the stem of some bamboo grass and starts to munch its spiky leaves.

Slowly, the panda shuffles out of the bamboo thicket. Eating bamboo makes her thirsty, so she sets off towards her favourite stream. Her great head sways from side to side as she plods along the valley bottom. Far above, thin white clouds are rolling back up the hillside. It is late spring and the rhododendron bushes are covered with beautiful pinky-red flowers.

4

The panda stretches and yawns again. Then she lumbers off down a small moss-covered track. She's always hungry, so she stops to nibble a few crocuses on the way.

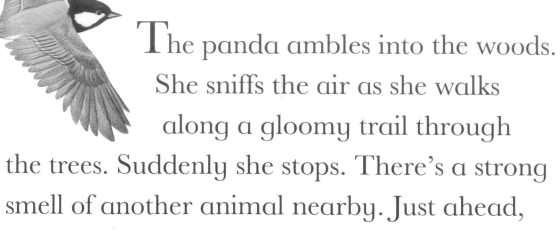

The panda ambles into the woods. She sniffs the air as she walks along a gloomy trail through the trees. Suddenly she stops. There's a strong smell of another animal nearby. Just ahead, the branches shake and rustle. Then, all at once, a startled face breaks through the bushes. It's a takin!

The panda snarls,
though she knows
the takin won't
attack her. But
the gentle takin
is scared and it
crashes off through
the undergrowth
in fright.

The panda reaches the stream and takes
a long drink of cool clear water. There's
a thick patch of bamboo growing nearby.
She often likes to rest here, with her back
against a mossy bank, while she
chomps on the lush green
bamboo shoots.

Gripping
the bamboo
stems tightly
in her paw, she
munches the
leaves and
crunches the
tough stalks.

The weeks pass and spring turns into summer. One day, as the panda rests on the branch of a tree, it begins to rain. The rain runs in little rivers down the paths. It drums on the tree trunks and the leaves. And it trickles down the panda's nose! She doesn't mind a fine, cold drizzle but she hates the heavy rain.

She climbs down
and finds a dry,
hollow tree trunk
to shelter in.
There, she has
a nap and waits
for the rain
to ease.

Winter arrives, covering the
mountains in a thick blanket of snow.
The panda has wandered towards the edge
of her territory, looking for some tasty bamboo
to eat. She pads down the hillside, leaving
pawprints in the freshly fallen snow.
She stops... she can hear strange
sounds ahead.

There are voices – coming closer! Then there's an excited shout! The panda is scared. She turns quickly and lumbers back into the safety of the forest.

When spring returns, fresh shoots of bamboo push their way through the warm soil and the streams become swollen with melted snow. One day the panda sees another black-and-white face peering through the undergrowth. It is a male panda. She grunts angrily and he moves away.

But the next day he's
there again. She begins
to feel more friendly
towards him. They
play together and
soon they mate.

One bright day, six months later, the panda sniffs around a little cave she has found. It seems warm and dry. She pulls in twigs, bamboo stems and fir branches to make a bed. Then she settles down, blocking the entrance with her body to keep the cave snug and safe.

Here, the
panda has her
baby cub. At first
he is tiny, blind
and helpless. But
he soon grows,
nourished by his
mother's rich,
warm milk.

The following winter is very cold.
Fierce winds blow down the mountainside.
Snow drifts into the bamboo thickets and
icicles hang over the stream. Even so, the
little panda cub grows big and strong. One day,
as he plays in the snow near his mother, there's
a flash of spotted fur in the bare branches
above. It's a leopard!

Quickly, the cub's mother rears up, baring her pointed fangs. She snarls fiercely, and the leopard bounds away across the powdery snow.

A whole year passes and it is spring once more. The giant panda and her cub are searching for the tastiest, tenderest young bamboo shoots on the whole mountain. As they wander down the hillside, they hear voices. Down in the valley bottom, hidden in a clump of trees, there's an orange tent on a platform of logs.

The tent belongs to some Chinese scientists who have been studying giant pandas for several weeks. They are checking that the pandas are safe and have enough bamboo to eat.

The panda cub is one and a half now and big enough to look after himself. One morning, he leaves his mother as she is ambling along her usual path to the stream. He is ready to find his own territory, in another part of the bamboo forest.

Index

When the page numbers are in **bold, like this,** it means you'll find the words under the folds.

KINGFISHER
An imprint of Larousse plc
Elsley House, 24–30 Great Titchfield Street,
London W1P 7AD

First published by Kingfisher 1994
2 4 6 8 10 9 7 5 3 1
Copyright © Larousse plc 1994

A CIP catalogue record for this book
is available from the British Library.

ISBN 1 85697 398 0

Typeset by Southern Positives and Negatives Limited, Lingfield Surrey
Colour separations by Scantrans Pte Ltd, Singapore
Printed in Singapore

Author: Philip Steele
Series editor: Sue Nicholson
Consultant: Mick Carmen, Headkeeper
Apes, Monkeys and Giant Pandas, London Zoo
Design: Ben White Associates
Art editor: Christina Fraser
Main illustrations: John Butler
Cartoons: Stephen Holmes
(Eunice McMullen)
Cover cartoons: Tony Kenyon
(B.L. Kearley Ltd)

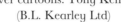